D1613170

Wild Flowers

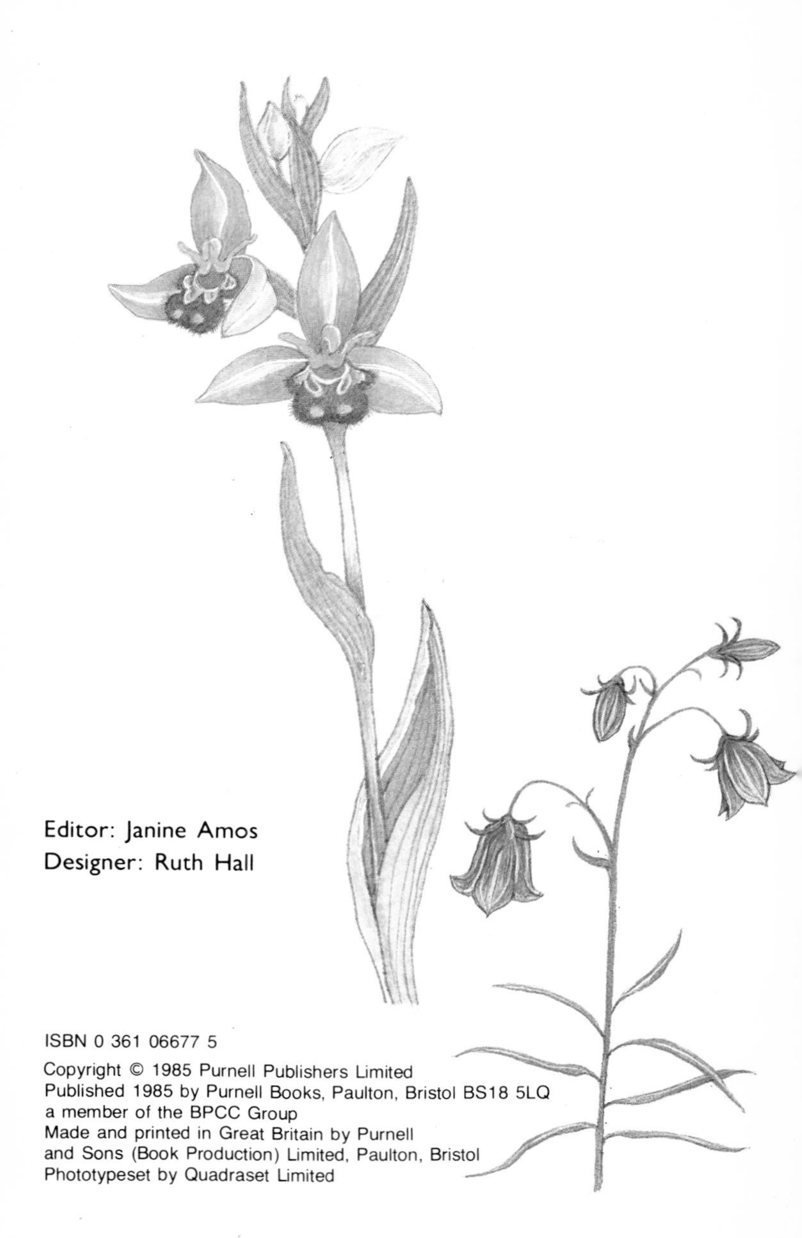

Editor: Janine Amos
Designer: Ruth Hall

ISBN 0 361 06677 5

Copyright © 1985 Purnell Publishers Limited
Published 1985 by Purnell Books, Paulton, Bristol BS18 5LQ
a member of the BPCC Group
Made and printed in Great Britain by Purnell
and Sons (Book Production) Limited, Paulton, Bristol
Phototypeset by Quadraset Limited

SPOT and STICK

Wild Flowers

Robin Kerrod

Illustrated by
Annie Russell

Purnell

Contents

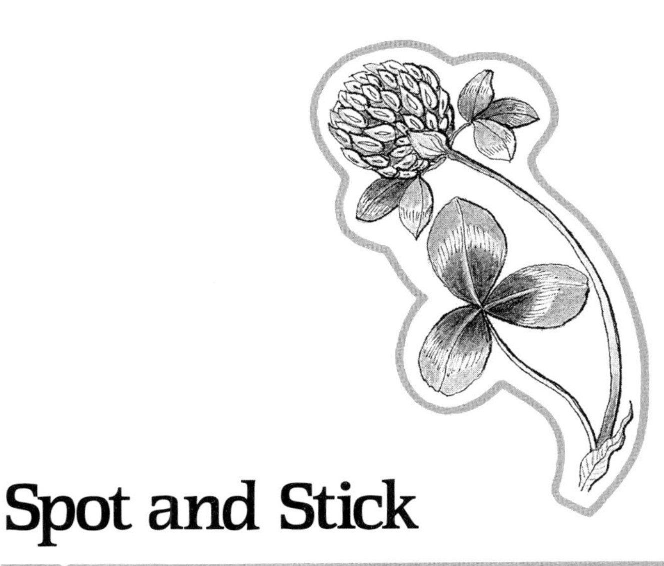

Spot and Stick

You will notice in the book that some flowers have a star next to their names. This tells you that there are stickers for these flowers. When you spot one of these flowers, cut out the sticker and stick it in a suitable place on the frieze. You can either leave the frieze at the back of the book, or cut it out and stick it on the wall.

Introduction

If you knew where to look, you could find several thousand different kinds of flowers around the countryside. Some are very common indeed. For example, you can find the daisy almost everywhere.

Other flowers are more particular about where they grow. You will find the yellow iris only in wet ground; the wood anemone in damp woods; and heather on the moors.

We call the place where a plant usually grows its habitat.

Using this Book

In this book we have divided up the flowers according to the habitat in which you are most likely to find them. In the garden, as weeds; in fields and along roadsides; in woodlands and hedgerows; in watery places; and in coastal regions. This is only a guide, because some plants can grow happily in different habitats.

When you spot a flower you want to identify, look first under the habitat in which you find it. Look at its shape and colour and try to match them with the pictures.

The main flower names given in this book are the common names. Underneath are the scientific, or botanical names, given in Latin. The first part of the Latin name gives the genus of the flower. This is the name of a group of similar plants. The second part gives the species of the flower. This refers to one particular kind of plant within the group.

Conservation

When you go flower-hunting, never dig up any plants. **It is against the law**. It is also against the law even to pick some very rare plants. All the flowers in this book are common, and you are usually free to pick them. But please don't pick too many. Make sure there are plenty left to seed.

Petals

Usually, the first thing you notice about a flower is its petals. They are often brightly coloured, and their main job is to attract insects. The picture above shows some of the different kinds of petals flowers have. It is always worth counting the petals of a flower and noting their shape. This often helps you identify it.

Flower-heads

Some plants have only a single flower growing at the top of the flower stem. But in most plants several flowers grow on the stem. They form a flower-head, or inflorescence. The picture opposite shows the main kinds of flower-heads. Look at the flower-head of the thistle, a composite. It is not a single flower made up of many petals, as you might think. It is a flower-head made up of many tiny florets. Each floret is a complete flower.

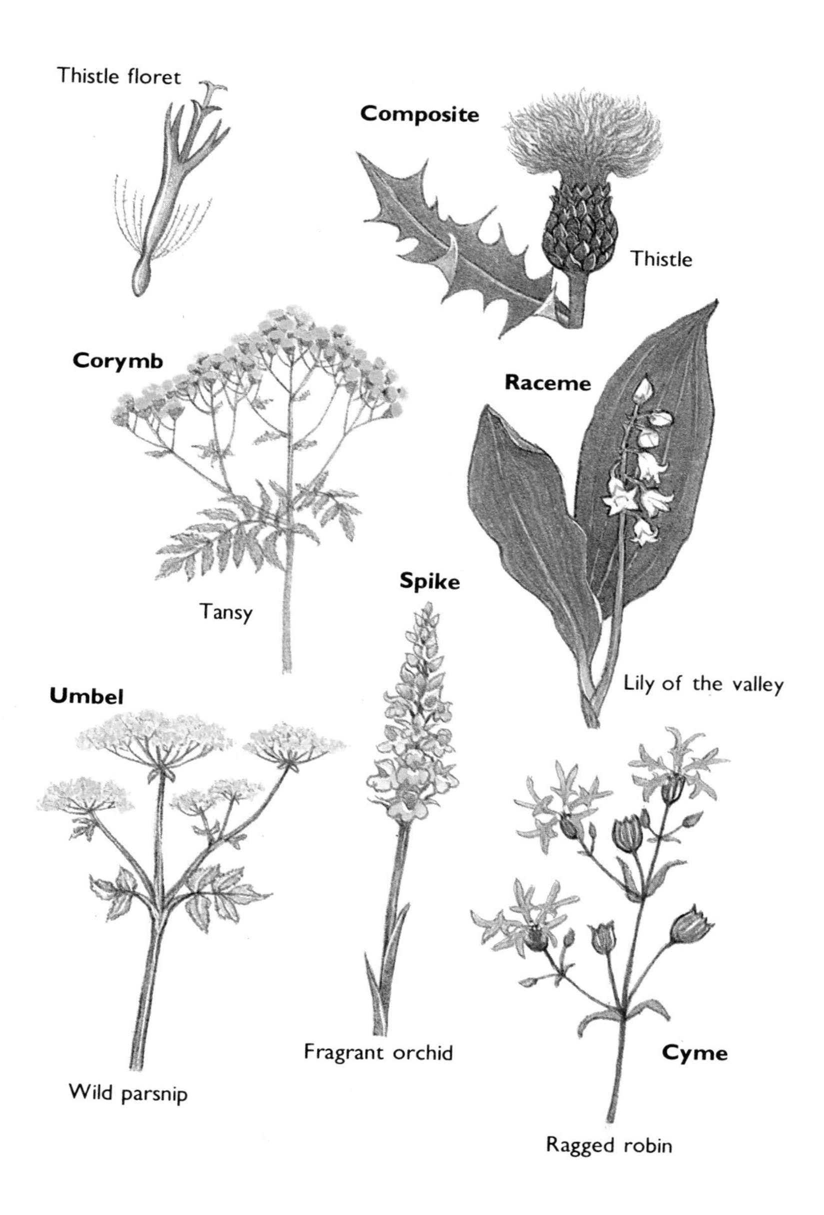
Thistle floret
Composite
Thistle
Corymb
Raceme
Tansy
Spike
Umbel
Lily of the valley
Fragrant orchid
Cyme
Wild parsnip
Ragged robin

Parts of a Flower

The petals are the most obvious parts of a flower. But there are several others, as you can see below.

The job of other parts is to make sure that the flower reproduces itself, or produces seeds from which similar plants can grow. Most plants have both male and female parts within the same flower. The male parts, called stamens, produce a yellow powder called pollen. The female parts, called pistils, produce the seeds.

To produce seeds, pollen from the stamens of another flower of the same kind must reach the pistils. This process is called pollination.

Pollination and Fertilization

Usually, bees and other insects carry the pollen from

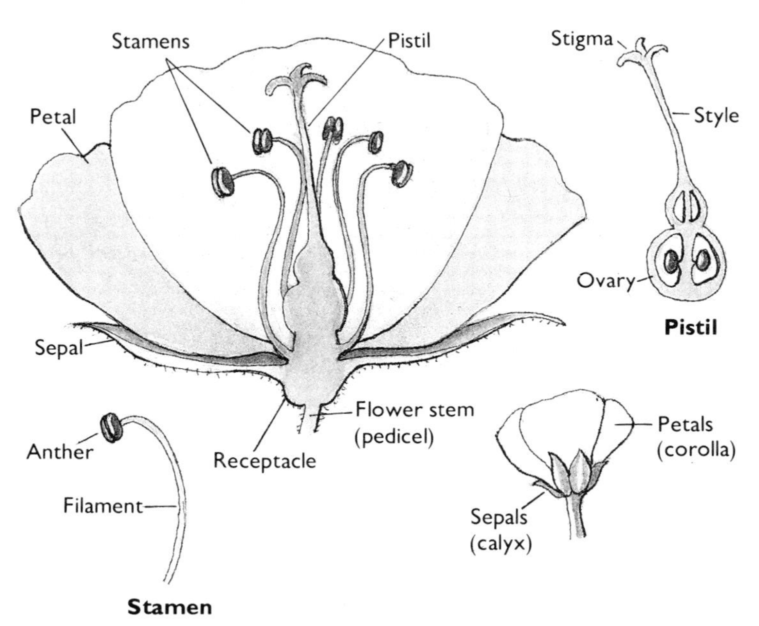

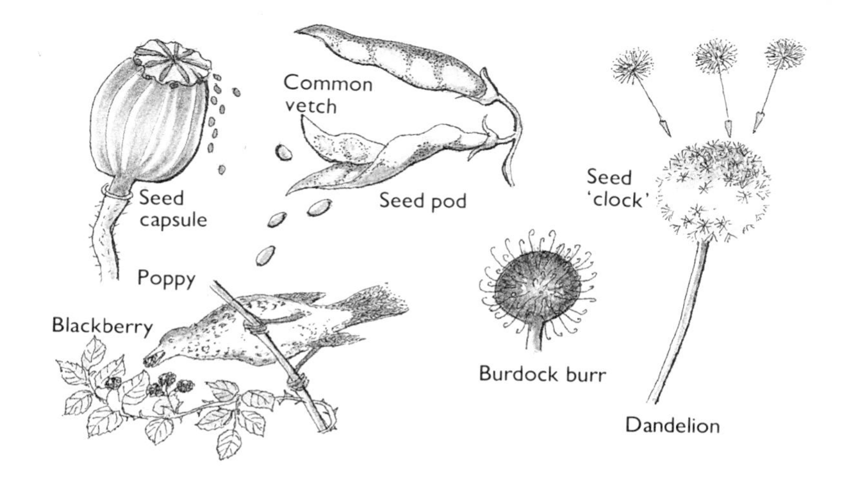

flower to flower. Flowers attract insects by their bright colours and the sweet nectar they contain. When the insects try to get at the nectar, they brush against the stamens and are dusted with pollen. Then they fly off to another flower. There, they brush against the stigmas, or sticky tops of the pistils, which pick up the pollen.

In some plants the wind carries the pollen from flower to flower. Their flowers are usually greenish with little scent. They do not need to attract insects.

When specks, or grains of pollen fall on a stigma of a flower, they begin to grow. They send tiny tubes down the style to reach the ovary (look at the picture opposite). Inside the ovary are the egg cells. Male cells from the pollen then travel down the tubes and combine with the egg cells. They fertilize the egg cells. After fertilization, the egg cells begin to grow and in time form seeds.

When the seeds and fruits are ripe, the plant uses one of several ways to scatter them far and wide. Some are shown above. Poppy and dandelion seeds blow away in the wind. Vetch seeds shoot out when their pods explode. Blackberry seeds are eaten by birds, which deposit the seeds in their droppings. Burdock seeds form inside burrs. These hook themselves to animals, which carry them away.

Garden Weeds

★

Creeping Buttercup

Ranunculus repens

Flowers: May–September
Height: 5–50 cm

This is a common lawn weed, also found in wet fields and meadows. It sends out runners in all directions, which root and form new plants. It likes damp conditions. The bulbous buttercup likes drier conditions.

Bulbous Buttercup

Ranunculus bulbosus

★

Common Daisy

Bellis perennis

Flowers: most of year
Height: up to 25 cm

The daisy is very common where the grass is short. The flowers have white or pink petals and yellow centres. They open early in the morning and close in the evening or in dull weather. The flowering stems are hairy.

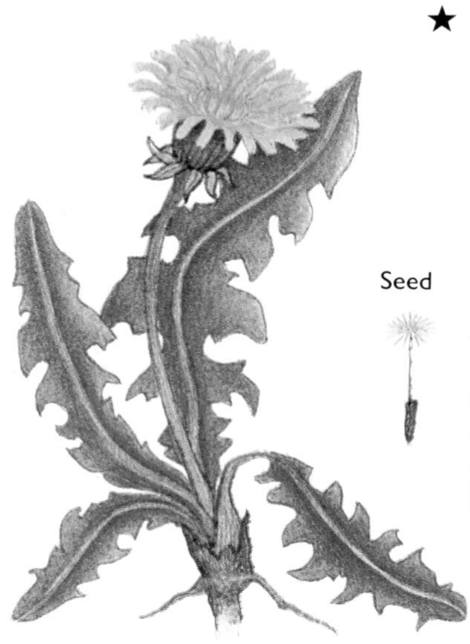

★ Dandelion

Taraxacum officinale

Flowers: March–October
Height: 5–30 cm

This plant gets its name from the sharp edges of its leaves, which look like a lion's teeth (dent de lion in French). Its hollow stems ooze a white juice when broken. Its seeds are contained in a fluffy seed-head 'clock'.

Yarrow

Achillea millefolium

Flowers: June–September
Height: 15–50 cm

The tiny, sweet-smelling flowers of the yarrow cluster into flat flower-heads. The leaves are split up, giving the plant a feathery appearance.

Chickweed

Stellaria media

Flowers: all year
Height: 5–36 cm

A favourite food of chickens and other poultry, chickweed has tiny, white flowers. The five petals are split, giving a ten-pointed 'star'.

Scarlet Pimpernel

Anagallis arvensis

Flowers: May–August
Height: 5–30 cm

A sprawling plant, with deep red flowers and dark green, glossy leaves.

Shepherd's Purse

Capsella bursa-pastoris

Flowers: all year
Height: 8–45 cm

The white flowers of this common weed cluster at the top of a long stem. The plant takes its name from the heart-shaped seed-pods, which look like the leather bags countryfolk once carried.

Groundsel

Senecio vulgaris

Flowers: all year
Height: 8–30 cm

The tiny flower-heads of this plant look rather like shaving brushes. They develop into white, fluffy seed-heads, which are wafted away by the slightest breeze.

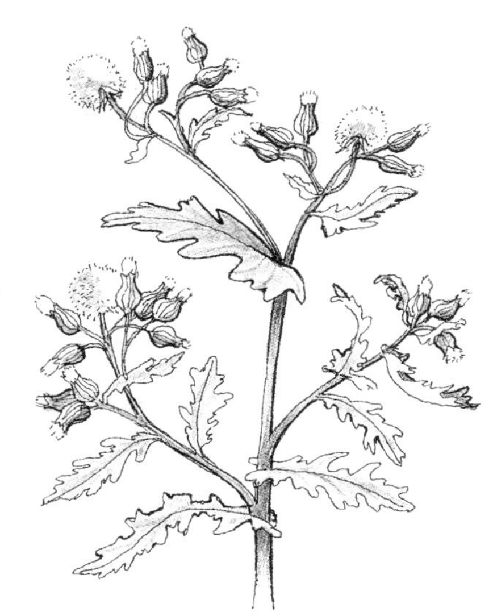

Common Field Speedwell

Veronica persica

Flowers: all year
Height: 10–30 cm

The tiny sky-blue flowers of this plant have four unequal petals. Look for the smaller, lower one which is paler than the others. There are 20 common speedwells.

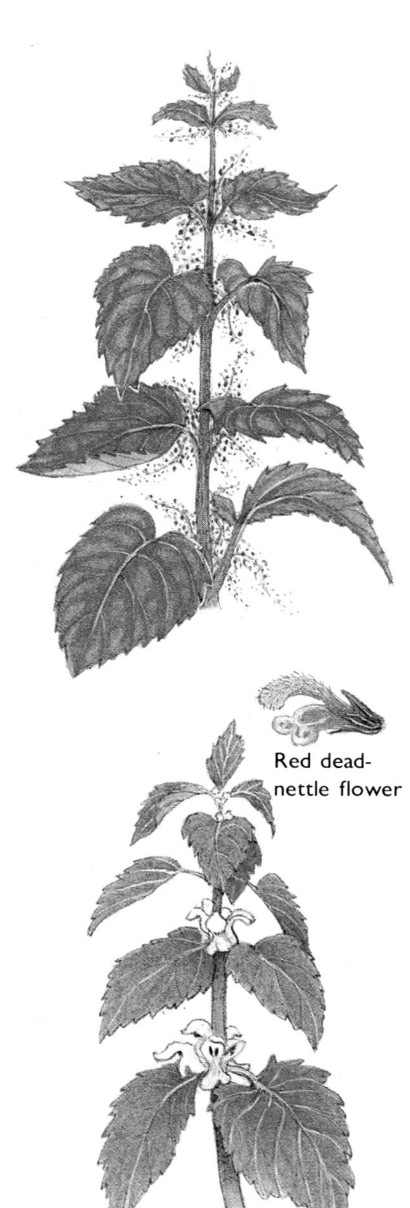
Red dead-nettle flower

Stinging Nettle

Urtica dioica

Flowers: May–September
Height: Up to 150 cm

The leaves of this plant are covered with fine, stinging hairs. The green flowers hang in spikes.

Red Dead-nettle

Lamium purpureum

Flowers: March–October
Height: 10–45 cm

This looks like the white dead-nettle but has pinkish-purple flowers.

White Dead-nettle

Lamium album

Flowers: May–December
Height: 20–60 cm

As its name suggests, this plant with nettle-like leaves does not sting. Its white flowers grow in rings around the plant stems. They have two 'lips', which bees enter to reach the nectar inside. The plant stems are square.

Broad-leaved Dock

Rumex obtusifolius

Flowers: June–October
Height: 50–100 cm

The flowers are green and grow in upright spikes. The leaves of docks provide relief from nettle stings when rubbed on the affected part.

Ribwort

Plantago lanceolata

Flowers: April–August
Height: up to 45 cm

The ribwort is another kind of plantain. It has similar flowers to the hoary plantain, but its leaves are long and narrow.

★
Hoary Plantain

Plantago media

Flowers: May–August
Height: up to 30 cm

Unlike the other kinds of plantains, it has a slight scent. It has broad, hairy leaves.

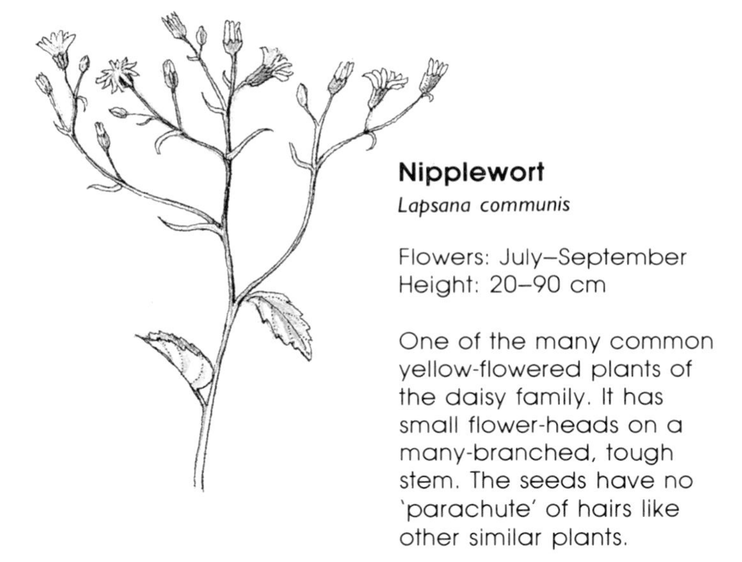

Nipplewort

Lapsana communis

Flowers: July–September
Height: 20–90 cm

One of the many common yellow-flowered plants of the daisy family. It has small flower-heads on a many-branched, tough stem. The seeds have no 'parachute' of hairs like other similar plants.

Jack-go-to-bed-at-noon

Tragopogon pratensis

Flowers: June–July
Height: 30–70 cm

By midday the large, yellow flowers of this plant are beginning to close. The flowers are carried on tall stems and form large 'clocks' like dandelions when they seed. The long bluish-green leaves, which cover the base of the stems, are very grass-like.

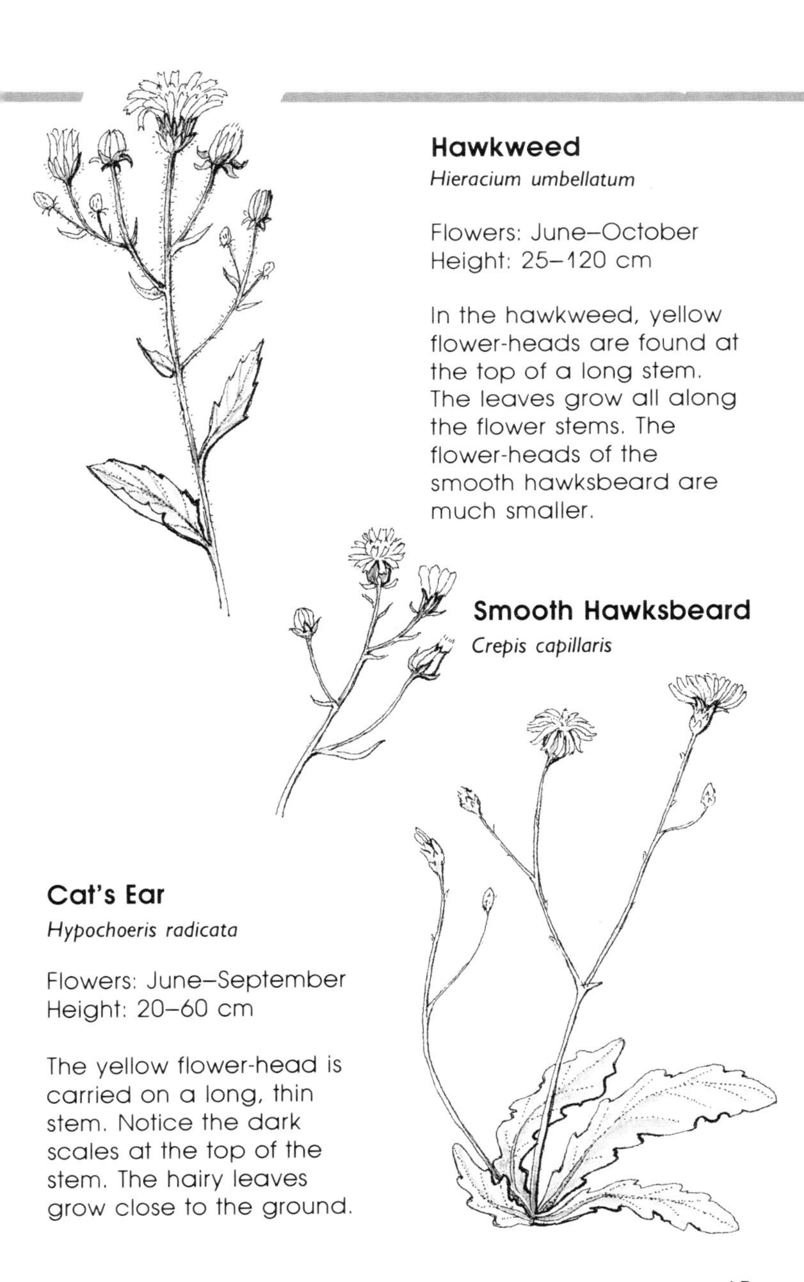

Hawkweed

Hieracium umbellatum

Flowers: June–October
Height: 25–120 cm

In the hawkweed, yellow flower-heads are found at the top of a long stem. The leaves grow all along the flower stems. The flower-heads of the smooth hawksbeard are much smaller.

Smooth Hawksbeard

Crepis capillaris

Cat's Ear

Hypochoeris radicata

Flowers: June–September
Height: 20–60 cm

The yellow flower-head is carried on a long, thin stem. Notice the dark scales at the top of the stem. The hairy leaves grow close to the ground.

★
Ox-eye Daisy
Leucanthemum vulgare

Flowers: June–August
Height: 20–60 cm

Each stem has a single flower which can be up to 5 cm across. Its leaves are a glossy, dark green and have toothed edges.

Feverfew
Tanacetum parthenium

Flowers: July–August
Height: 25–60 cm

The flower-heads grow together on branches from the stem. The white petals are short and wide.

Colt's Foot
Tussilago farfara

Flowers: March–April
Height: 15–30 cm

A very early-flowering daisy. The flowers grow on thick stems covered in scales. The plant is named after the hoof-shape of its broad leaves.

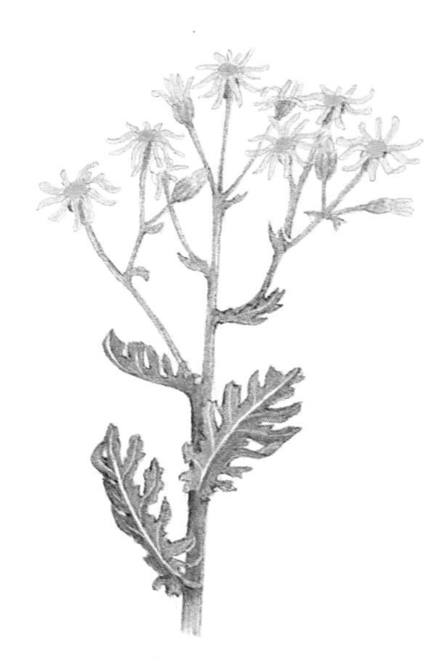

Common Ragwort

Senecio jacobaea

Flowers: June–October
Height: 30–120 cm

This common weed is found in most places, except on high ground. It gets its name from the ragged appearance of the dark green leaves.

Tansy

Tanacetum vulgare

Flowers: July–September
Height: 30–105 cm

The flowers of these daisies are yellow and do not have the outer petals like other daisies.

★

Scentless Mayweed

Matricaria perforata

Flowers: July–September
Height: 15–60 cm

Unlike many of its close relatives, this plant does not smell strongly when bruised. Each stem has a single white flower. The leaves are fern-like.

Sorrel

Rumex acetosa

Flowers: May–June
Height: up to 100 cm

Sorrels are related to docks. Their tiny, reddish flowers grow on long spikes. The leaves, which often turn red in the autumn, have an acid flavour. Sorrel was once used as a vegetable.

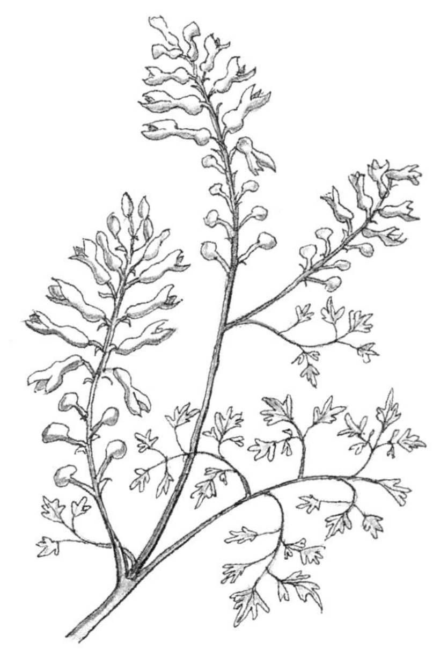

Common Fumitory

Fumaria officinalis

Flowers: May–September
Height: up to 50 cm

This plant has 30 or more dark pink flowers which grow in long spikes. The fruits are small, round nuts containing a single seed. The delicate-looking leaves are grey-green.

Silverweed

Potentilla anserina

Flowers: May–August
Height: 5–25 cm

Silverweed gets its name from the silky hairs on its leaves which give them a silvery appearance. The large flowers are bright yellow. It sends out creeping runners, rather like the strawberry.

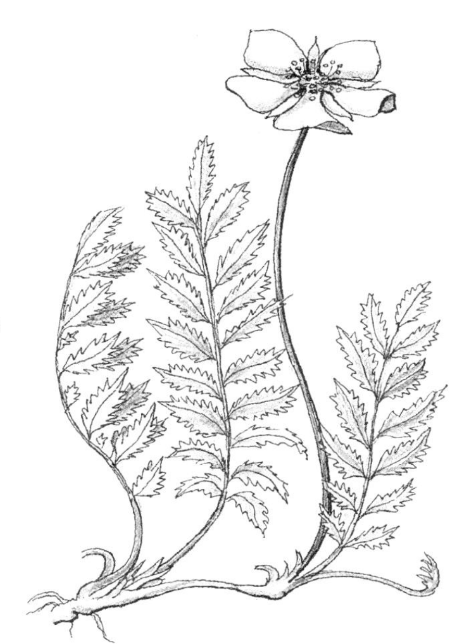

Field Scabious

Knautia arvensis

Flowers: June–September
Height: 25–100 cm

Field scabious has round flower-heads of mauve or blue. In full flower the stamens stand out like pins in a pin-cushion. The plant is sometimes called 'lady's pin-cushion'.

★
Rosebay Willowherb
Epilobium angustifolium

Flowers: June–September
Height: up to 120 cm

Rosebay willowherb is often found on waste ground. It gets its name from its long, narrow leaves which look like those of the willow tree. In autumn the long seed-pods split and release white fluffy seeds.

★
Field Poppy
Papaver rhoeas

Flowers: May–October
Height: 20–60 cm

The bright red flowers of this common poppy can measure up to 10 cm across. It is not so common on farmland as it once was because of the widespread use of weedkillers. The stems are hairy. The seed-capsule has holes around the top, like a pepperpot, to allow the tiny black seeds to escape. The seed-capsule of the Welsh poppy splits down the sides to release the seeds.

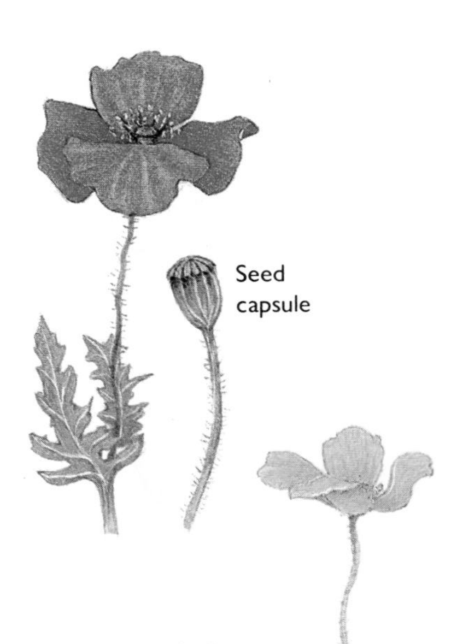

Welsh Poppy
Meconopsis cambrica

Dove's Foot Crane's Bill

Geranium molle

Flowers: April–September
Height: 10–40 cm

One of several plants closely related to the garden geranium. It has delicate pink flowers, and broad, hairy leaves. Notice the seeds, which are contained in a pointed column. Herb-Robert is a similar plant, but the flowers have more rounded petals.

Herb-Robert

Geranium robertianum

Harebell

Campanula rotundifolia

Flowers: July–September
Height: 15–40 cm

A delicate plant with blue bell-shaped flowers. The flowers hang on fine stems and nod in the breeze. In Scotland the plant is known as the bluebell.

Red Clover

Trifolium pratense

Flowers: May–September
Height: up to 60 cm

Red clover is one of the plants called a trefoil. This means that its leaves are made up of three leaflets. The reddish-purple flower-head grows without a stalk between leaves at the top of the stem.

Black Medick

Medicago lupulina

Flowers: May–August
Height: 5–50 cm

Another trefoil plant. It has tiny clover-like yellow flower-heads and black seeds.

Lesser Burdock

Arctium minus

Flowers: July–September
Height: 60–120 cm

This tall plant grows purple thistle-like flower-heads. They are covered with tiny hooked burrs.

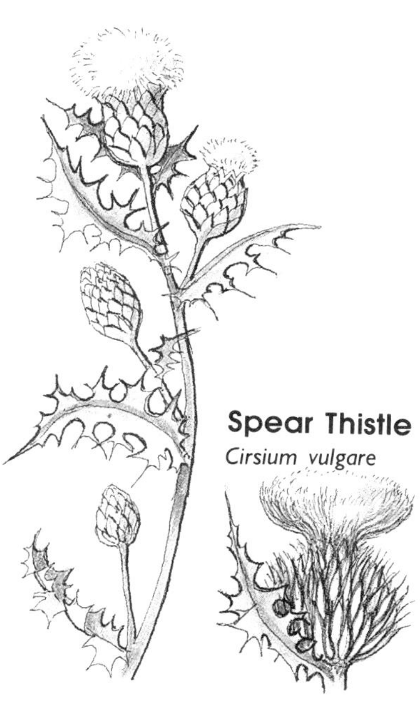

Spear Thistle

Cirsium vulgare

Creeping Thistle

Cirsium arvense

Flowers: July–September
Height: 30–150 cm

This tall plant has prickly stems and leaves. It is a common weed on farmland and its strong scent attracts butterflies. The spear thistle is well-named because of its vicious-looking spiky leaves. Like the other thistles illustrated, it has a purplish flower-head.

Common Knapweed

Centaurea nigra

Flowers: June–September
Height: 30–60 cm

Also called hardheads, this has a thistle-like purple flower-head. The plant has hairy leaves, which are long and narrow.

Bird's Foot Trefoil

Lotus corniculatus

Flowers: May–September
Height: 10–40 cm

This common trailing plant has bright yellow flowers. The leaf is made up of three leaflets, like other trefoil plants, with another pair near the stem. The seeds develop in thin pods, which look like a bird's claw.

Dark Mullein

Verbascum nigrum

Flowers: June–September
Height: 50–120 cm

This plant likes chalk soil. It has tall spikes of deep yellow flowers. The leaves are soft and felt-like.

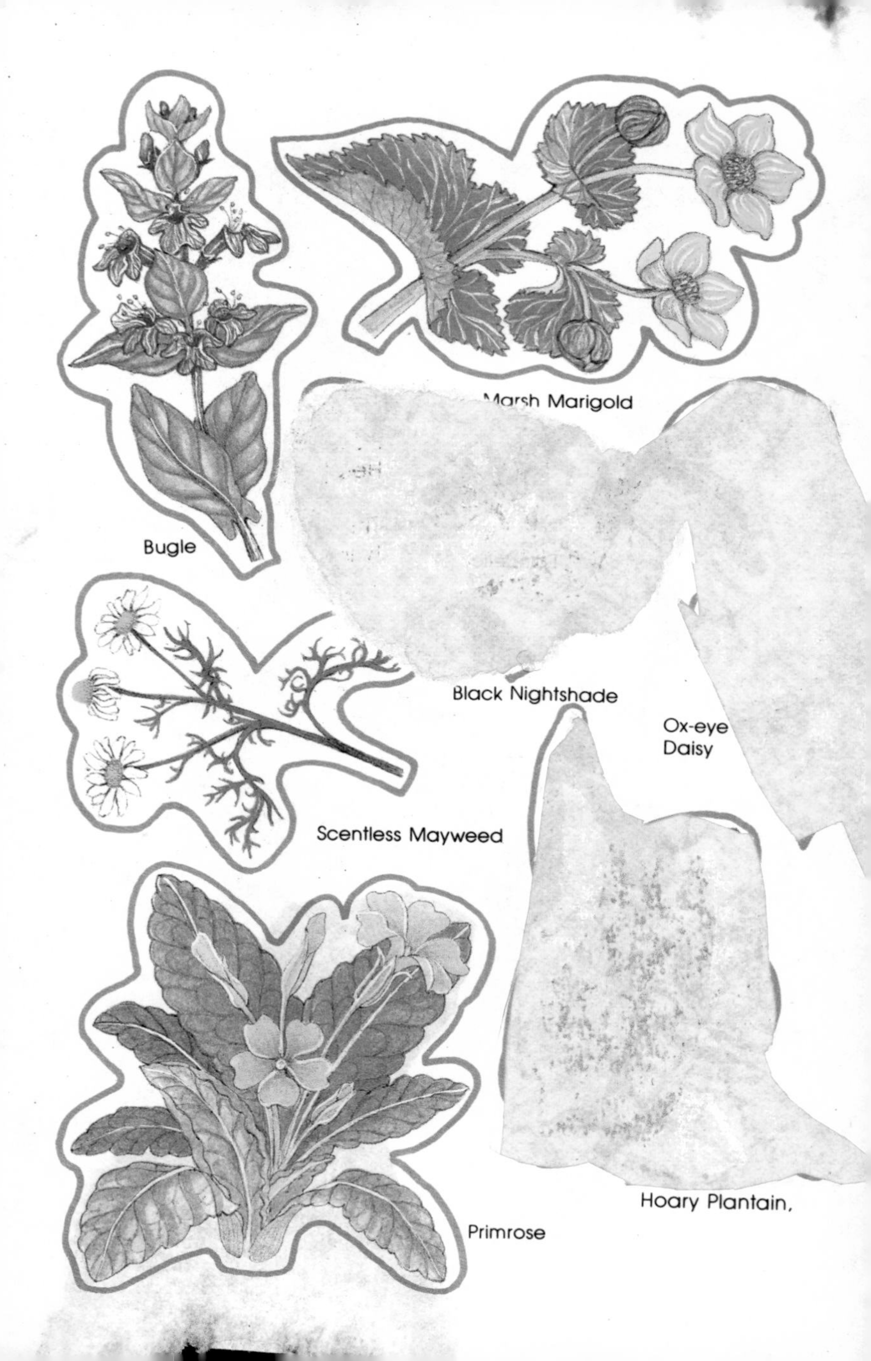
Bugle
Marsh Marigold
Black Nightshade
Ox-eye
Daisy
Scentless Mayweed
Hoary Plantain,
Primrose

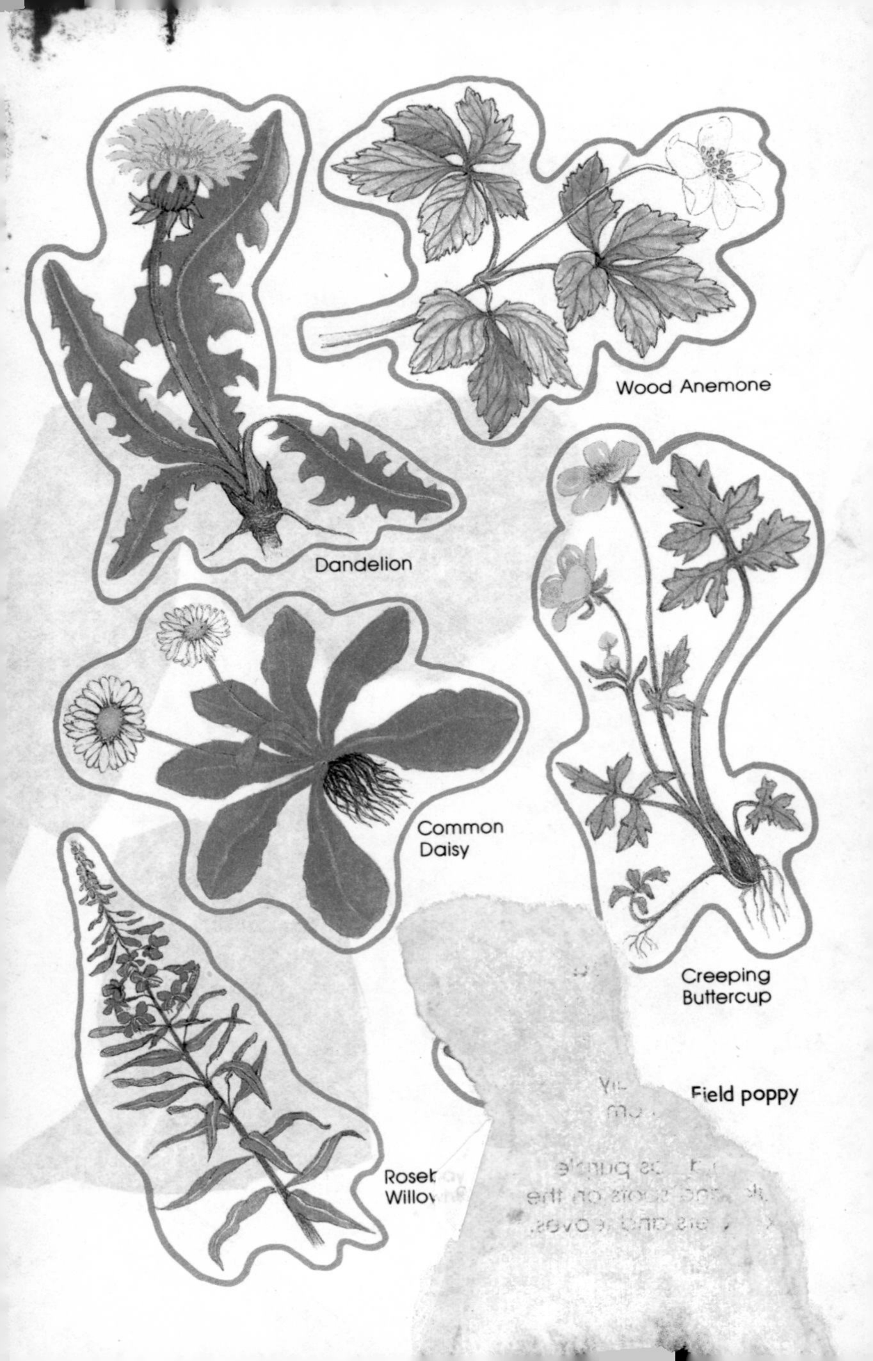
Dandelion
Wood Anemone
Common
Daisy
Creeping
Buttercup
Field poppy
Roseb
Willow

Bee Orchid

Ophrys apifera

Flowers: June–July
Height: 15–60 cm

Another chalk-lover is the bee orchid. This plant is so-called because each flower looks as if a bumble bee has landed on it. The 'bee' is actually the furry lower lip of the flower.

Fragrant Orchid

Gymnadenia conopsea

Flowers: June–August
Height: 15–40 cm

The flowers grow in thick spikes and have the spicy scent of cloves. Notice the spur on each one. They attract large numbers of moths and butterflies.

Common Spotted Orchid

Dactylorhiza fuchsii

Flowers: June–July
Height: 15–60 cm

This orchid has purple streaks and spots on the pink flowers and leaves.

Gorse

Ulex europaeus

Flowers: all year
Height: up to 2 metres

Also called furze, this spiky shrub has golden yellow flowers which smell like almonds. It belongs to the pea family and the seeds grow in short pods.

Broom

Cytisus scoparius

Flowers: May–June
Height: up to 2 metres

Broom looks rather like a smooth gorse. It has yellow flowers and produces its seeds in black pods. When ripe, the pods explode and scatter their seeds over quite a distance.

Bell Heather

Erica cineria

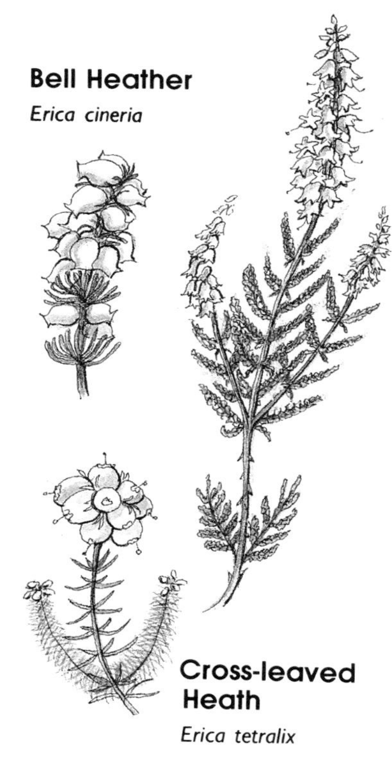

Heather

Calluna vulgaris

Flowers: July–September
Height: up to 60 cm

Also called ling, this heather is a small plant found on heaths and moors. Its tiny purple flowers cluster into spikes. Look for 'lucky' white heather. Bell heather has reddish-purple bell-shaped flowers on long spikes. Cross-leaved heath has bell-shaped reddish-purple flowers at the stem tips.

Cross-leaved Heath

Erica tetralix

Milkwort

Polygala vulgaris

Flowers: May–September
Height: 5–10 cm

The blue flowers of this common plant are unusual. They have two long, blue, inner sepals, which almost cover the flower petals. The flowers may also be pink or white.

Lesser Celandine

Ranunculus ficaria

Flowers: March–May
Height: 6–15 cm

These shiny, yellow flowers bloom in spring in damp, shady places. Each has up to 12 narrow petals. The dark green leaves are heart-shaped.

Bluebell

Hyacinthoides non-scripta

Flowers: April–June
Height: 20–50 cm

The bell-shaped flowers of the bluebell have a sweet scent. They hang on one side of a tall stem. Sometimes the flowers are pink or white.

★

Wood Anemone

Anemone nemorosa

Flowers: March–May
Height: 5–30 cm

Wood anemones are also called windflowers. They sometimes form a thick carpet in woods in the spring. A ring of three leaves grows high up on the flower stem and the flowers have pink-streaked sepals.

Oxlip

Primula elatior

★

Primrose

Primula vulgaris

Flowers: March–May
Height: up to 15 cm

Another spring flower. The pale yellow flowers grow from the centre of a rosette of wrinkled leaves. The pale yellow flowers of the oxlip grow in a cluster on the flower stem. The cowslip, which grows in grasslands, is quite similar, but has smaller flowers.

Bilberry

Vaccinium myrtillus

Flowers: April–June
Height: up to 60 cm

The bilberry is also called the blaeberry or whortleberry. It is a low plant of woods and moors, and may form thick carpets ('bilberry moors'). The pink, drooping, bell-shaped flowers ripen into blue-grey berries.

Greater Stitchwort

Stellaria holostea

Flowers: April–June
Height: 15–60 cm

The greater stitchwort has grass-like leaves and white star-shaped flowers with divided petals.

Sweet Violet

Viola odorata

Flowers: January–April
Height: up to 6 cm

This is the only violet with a sweet scent. The flowers are sometimes white instead of the usual violet-blue. Violets grow in clumps and have heart-shaped leaves. The violet flower has five violet-blue petals. The lowest petal is larger and longer, forming a lip.

Foxglove

Digitalus purpurea

Flowers: June–August
Height: 60–150 cm

The foxglove produces tall stems of tube-like flowers. They are pinkish-purple in colour and have white and purple spots inside, which guide bees to the mouth of the flower. The large leaves are grey-green and soft. This plant is **poisonous**.

Lords and Ladies

Arum maculatum

Flowers: April–May
Height: 30–45 cm

This plant has many other names, including cuckoo pint, wild arum, and Jack-in-the-pulpit. The flowers are hidden in a leaf-like cloak, below a purple spike. The red berries are **poisonous**.

★
Bugle

Ajuga reptans

Flowers: May–July
Height: 10–30 cm

This plant belongs to the mint family. It spreads thickly by means of long stems. The blue flowers grow in rings around the stems.

Ramsons

Allium ursinum

Flowers: April–August
Height: up to 45 cm

A common plant in woods. Each stem has a head of white star-shaped flowers, and the leaves are broad and bright green. The plant smells of garlic when crushed.

Goldenrod

Solidago virgaurea

Flowers: July–August
Height: up to 60 cm

The ragged yellow flowers of this daisy-like plant grow in small clusters. The taller Canadian goldenrod, which often escapes from gardens, has thick plumes of yellow flowers.

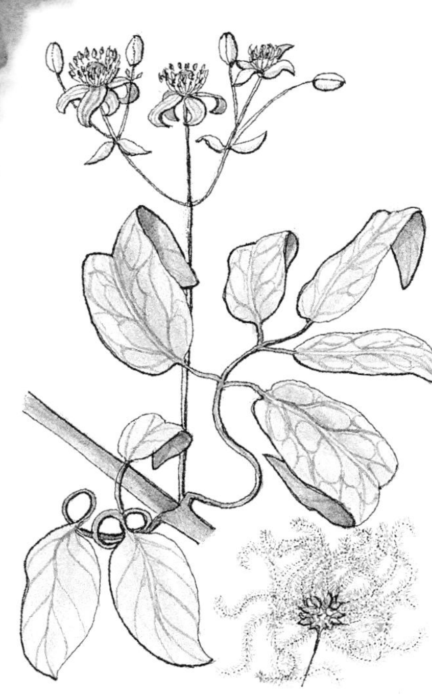

Traveller's Joy

Clematis vitalba

Flowers: July–August
Height: up to 30 metres

Look for traveller's joy twisting its way amongst bushes and trees in the hedgerows. In summer its white flowers grow in sprays and in autumn feathery seeds cover the whole plant. It is also called old man's beard.

Hedge Bindweed

Calystegia sepium

Flowers: July–September
Height: up to 3 metres

This climber has pure white trumpet-like flowers. It climbs anti-clockwise and can be found growing near hedges and walls in waste places. Ordinary bindweed has pink flowers with white stripes.

Bindweed
Convolvulus arvensis

Ivy

Hedera helix

Flowers: September–
November
Height: up to 30 metres

This climber has dark green, shiny leaves. It flowers very late in the year and then becomes alive with bees, wasps and flies, which are attracted to the nectar. The flowers are greenish-yellow and form a round head. They turn into black berries which are **poisonous**.

Honeysuckle

Lonicera periclymenum

Flowers: June–September
Height: up to 6 metres

The honeysuckle is a strong climber in woods and hedgerows. Its orange-yellow flowers are trumpet-shaped with long stamens. They have a sweet scent.

Dog Rose

Rosa canina

Flowers: June–July
Height: up to 3 metres

The dog rose is a strong climber with thorny stems. Look for its pink flowers in early summer and in autumn for the bright red fruits, called rose hips.

Blackberry

Rubus fruticosus

Flowers: May–September
Height: up to 90 cm

The blackberry has strong, prickly stems which arch high into the air and take root where they touch the ground. Its berries are ripe in the autumn and are good to eat. Another name for the blackberry is bramble.

Woody Nightshade

Solanum dulcamara

Flowers: June–September
Height: up to 2 metres

This plant is also called bittersweet. Like all nightshades, it belongs to the potato family. Its red berries are **poisonous**.

★ Black Nightshade

Solanum nigrum

Flowers: July–September
Height: up to 60 cm

This is not a climber. Its black berries are **poisonous**.

Deadly Nightshade

Atropa belladonna

Flowers: June–August
Height: up to 150 cm

This tall plant has purplish-brown bell-shaped flowers. The black fruit is deadly **poisonous**.

Garlic Mustard

Alliaria petiolata

Flowers: April–June
Height: up to 120 cm

This is also called Jack-by-the-hedge. The white flower-heads grow at the top of the stem. Seeds develop in narrow pods.

Common Vetch

Vicia sativa

Flowers: May–September
Height: 15–120 cm

This plant belongs to the pea family. It has pinkish-purple flowers and its seeds grow in pods. Tendrils grow at the end of the leaves. The tufted vetch is similar, but the flowers are bluish-purple and grow in long spikes.

Tufted Vetch

Vicia cracca

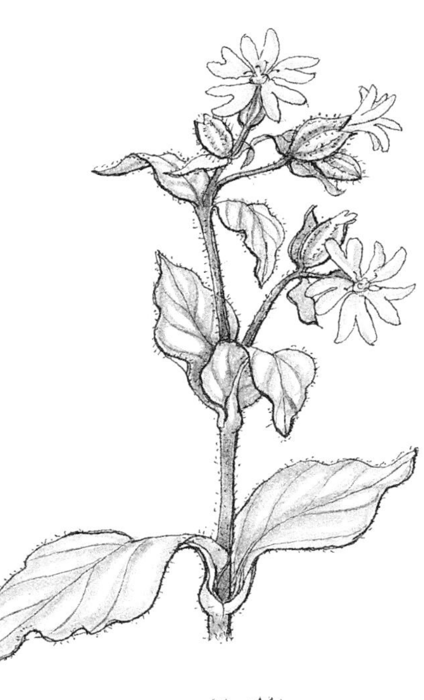

Red Campion

Silene dioica

Flowers: May–June
Height: 30–90 cm

The red petals of this flower are divided. The stems are sticky and hairy. The white campion is similar but has white flowers. The bladder campion has a scent.

Bladder Campion

Silene vulgaris

Cow Parsley

Anthriscus sylvestris

Flowers: April–June
Height: 60–120 cm

Cow parsley is the earliest of the three common wild parsleys to flower. The others are rough chervil and hedge parsley. They all have their white flowers clustered in umbrella-shaped heads. Their leaves are almost fern-like.

Purple Loosestrife

Lythrum salicaria

Flowers: June–August
Height: 60–120 cm

The bright purple flowers of this water-loving plant grow in tall spikes. Sets of six long-petalled flowers grow in a ring around the square flower stem.

Cuckoo Flower

Cardamine pratensis

Flowers: April–June
Height: 15–60 cm

This plant is also called lady's smock. The pink flowers have four petals arranged in the shape of a cross. The plant forms seed-pods which explode to release the ripe seeds.

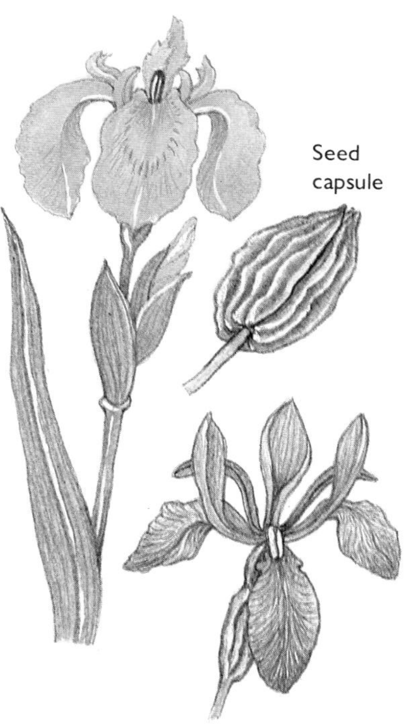

Yellow Iris

Iris pseudacorus

Flowers: May–July
Height: 40–150 cm

The yellow iris grows in wet woods, marshy ground and near rivers and ditches. It is also called yellow flag. The leaves of the stinking iris have a strange smell when crushed.

Stinking Iris

Iris foetidissima

Marsh Marigold

Caltha palustris

Flowers: March–July
Height: 30–60 cm

Look for the marsh marigold in damp places. Its glossy, golden yellow flowers measure up to 5 cm across. The leaves are shiny, dark green and heart-shaped.

Sundew

Drosera rotundifolia

Flowers: June–July
Height: 6–25 cm

The sundew grows in bogs and on wet moors. Notice the round leaves covered with sticky, red hairs. The plant feeds by trapping insects as they settle on the leaves. Its tiny, white flowers grow on long, thin stems.

Ragged Robin

Lychnis flos-cuculi

Flowers: May–July
Height: 30–70 cm

The plant gets its name from its ragged petals. Pairs of long, narrow leaves grow up the flower stem. The flowers are usually pink, but white ones can be found.

Cranberry

Vaccinium oxycoccos

Flowers: June–August
Height: up to 30 cm

The cranberry is another bog plant. It produces red pear-shaped berries on long stalks. Notice the curved, pink petals. Cranberries are eaten in pies and jellies.

Meadowsweet

Filipendula ulmaria

Flowers: June–September
Height: 60–120 cm

The tiny cream-coloured flowers of meadowsweet grow in clusters and give off a sweet smell. The flower stems are reddish-brown and the large leaves dark green. Meadowsweet grows in marshes, water meadows and near ditches.

White Water-lily

Nymphaea alba

Flowers: June–August
Height: up to 2.5 metres

The large white flowers of this floating plant are made up of 20 or more petals.

Yellow Water-lily

Nuphar lutea

Frogbit

Hydrocharis morsus-ranae

Water Crowfoot

Ranunculus aquatilis

Flowers: May–June
Height: up to 120 cm

Water crowfoot is found in streams, ponds and ditches. It has flat leaves that float on the surface as well as thread-like leaves underwater. The river water crowfoot has larger flowers and no floating leaves.

Bladderwort

Utricularia vulgaris

Flowers: July–August
Height: 15–45 cm

Bladderwort floats in lakes, ponds and ditches. Its thread-like leaves have tiny bladders, which trap creatures such as water fleas for food.

Bogbean

Menyanthes trifoliata

Flowers: May–July
Height: up to 30 cm

The bogbean grows in bogs and shallow ponds. The pinkish-white flowers have five petals that are fringed with white hairs.

Glasswort

Salicornia ramosissima

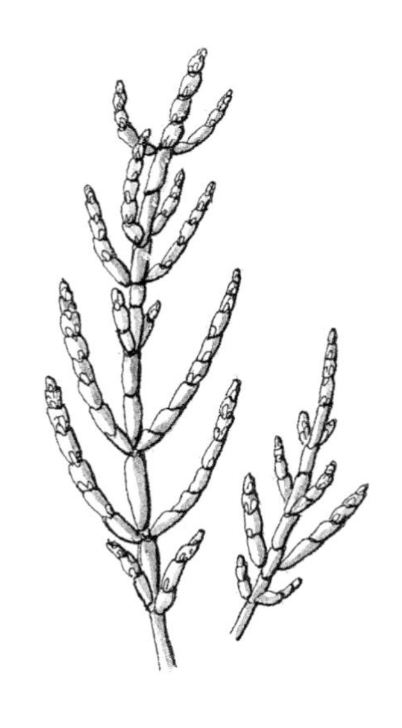

Flowers: August–September
Height: up to 30 cm

This is also called marsh samphire. It is a plant that grows in salt marshes and on seashores. The glossy green stems and branches gradually turn reddish-purple as they grow. Tiny yellowish flowers appear along the branches. This plant was once used for making glass.

Thrift

Armeria maritima

Flowers: April–August
Height: up to 15 cm

This is also called sea pink. Its scented pink flowers grow in a tuft on long stems, from clumps of grass-like leaves.

Yellow-horned Poppy

Glaucium flavum

Flowers: June–September
Height: 30–90 cm

The 'horn' on this plant is actually a long seed-capsule. It grows when the bright yellow flowers die.

Sea Purslane

Halimione portulacoides

Flowers: July–September
Height: up to 80 cm

This plant grows in salt marshes. It sends up thick spikes of yellow-orange flowers in summer. The leaves are silvery.

Sea Holly

Eryngium maritimum

Flowers: July–August
Height: 30–90 cm

The spiny leaves of this plant are blue-green in colour. The flower-head is blue and prickly, like that of a thistle.

Index